Grade 4 Level 4 Early intermediate **Piano**

Improve your sight-reading!

Paul Harris

FABER 𝆑𝆑 MUSIC

Practice chart

	Comments (from you, your teacher or parent)	Done!
Stage 1		
Stage 2		
Stage 3		
Stage 4		
Stage 5		
Stage 6		
Stage 7		
Stage 8		
Stage 9		

Teacher's name _____

Telephone _____

Many thanks to Jean Cockburn, Claire Dunham, Graeme Humphrey and Diana Jackson for their invaluable help, and particular thanks to Lesley Rutherford whose editorial skills and perpetual encouragement went far beyond the call of duty.

© 2008 by Faber Music Ltd.
This edition first published in 2008 by Faber Music Ltd.
Bloomsbury House, 74–77 Great Russell Street, London WC1B 3DA
Music setting by Graham Pike
Cover and page design by Susan Clarke
Cover illustration by Drew Hillier
Printed in England by Caligraving Ltd
All rights reserved

ISBN10: 0-571-53304-3 (US edition 0-571-53314-0)
EAN13: 978-0-571-53304-6 (US edition 978-0-571-53314-5)

To buy Faber Music publications or to find out about the full range of titles available please contact your local music retailer or Faber Music sales enquiries:
Faber Music Ltd, Burnt Mill, Elizabeth Way, Harlow CM20 2HX
Tel: +44 (0) 1279 82 89 82   Fax: +44 (0) 1279 82 89 83
sales@fabermusic.com   fabermusic.com

Introduction

Being a good sight-reader is so important and it needn't be difficult!
If you work through this book carefully – always making sure that you
really understand each exercise before you play it, you'll never have
problems learning new pieces or doing well at sight-reading in exams!

Using the workbook

1 Rhythmic exercises

Make sure you have grasped these fully before you go on to the
melodic exercises: it is vital that you really know how the rhythms
work. There are a number of ways to do these examples – see *Improve
your sight-reading* Grade 1 for more details.

2 Melodic exercises

These exercises use just the notes and rhythms for the Stage, and also
give some help with fingering. If you want to sight-read fluently and
accurately, get into the habit of working through each exercise in the
following ways before you begin to play it:

- Make sure you understand the rhythm and counting. Clap the
  exercise through.
- Look at the shape of the tune, particularly the highest and lowest
  notes and think about the best way to finger it.
- Try to hear the piece through in your head. Always play the first
  note to help.

3 Prepared pieces

Work your way through the questions first, as these will help you to
think about or 'prepare' the piece. Don't begin playing until you are
pretty sure you know exactly how the piece goes.

4 Going solo!

It is now up to you to discover the clues in this series of practice
pieces. Give yourself about a minute and do your best to understand
the piece before you play. Check the rhythms and hand position, and
try to hear the piece in your head.

Always remember to feel the pulse and to keep going steadily once
you've begun.

Good luck and happy sight-reading!

Terminology:
Bar = measure

Stage 1

Whenever you speak you put expression into what you say. Do the same with your sight-reading performances! As you're preparing the piece, as well as thinking about the notes, shape and rhythm, think about how you'll interpret the piece – or play it musically. You will need to think about:

- Does it require crisp or more gentle and sustained playing?

- Do you need to use accents in addition to those that are marked?

- Is it a tune with accompaniment? (Balance of hands will be important if so.)

- Are both hands equally important?

- What would be an effective speed?

Rhythmic exercises

Always count two bars before you begin each exercise – one out loud and one silently.

Melodic exercises

Prepared pieces

1 What are the clues to the character of this piece?

2 Should the notes be played *legato* or detached?

3 Think about your fingering and changing hand position.

4 Tap the rhythm of the piece, hands together.

5 Play the first note of each hand and then hear the piece in your head as best you can.

6 Do you feel confident that you'll give an accurate performance?

1 What are the main clues to the character of this piece?

2 What interval is formed by the first two notes of the left hand?

3 How many bars are based on scale and arpeggio patterns? (Play the scale and arpeggio.)

4 Look through the piece for changes of hand position.

5 Tap the rhythm of the piece, hands together.

6 Play the first note of each hand and then hear the piece in your head as best you can.

Going solo!

Don't forget to prepare each piece carefully before you play it.

Stage 2

Rhythmic exercises

Always count two bars before you begin each exercise – one out loud
and one silently, then continue to feel the pulse strongly.

Melodic exercises

Don't forget to count two bars before you begin each melodic
exercise as well.

Prepared pieces

1 What is the key of this piece? Play the scale and arpeggio.

2 Are there any repeated patterns?

3 What does 'swing the quavers' mean? Tap the rhythm of each hand separately. Now tap the rhythms of both hands together.

4 Look carefully for changes of hand position in the right hand. How many are there?

5 Look at the final chord in the right hand. Now play it.

6 Play the first note in each hand and hear the piece in your head as best you can.

Cool (swing the quavers)

1

1 What is the key of this piece? Play the scale and arpeggio.

2 Where does the right hand change position?

3 Are there any repeated patterns?

4 Clap the left hand and think the right hand silently.

5 Can you spot any patterns based on scales?

6 Play the first note in each hand and hear the piece in your head as best you can.

Moderato

2

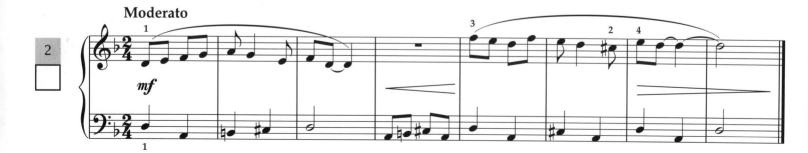

Going solo!

Stage 3

Rhythmic exercises

Always count two bars before you begin each exercise – one out loud
and one silently.

Melodic exercises

Prepared pieces

1 What is the key of this piece? Play the scale and arpeggio.

2 Think how you will finger the chords in bars 1–4 and bars 7-8 (left hand).

3 Are there any repeated patterns?

4 What will you count? Tap the rhythm of each hand separately then both together.

5 Play the first note of each hand and then hear the piece through in your head.

6 How will you give a waltz-like performance?

1 What is the key of this piece? Play the scale and arpeggio.

2 Can you see any bars that are not based on scale or arpeggio patterns?

3 Search for the E flats and store them up in your mind.

4 How will the ♩♪♪♪ in the final bar affect your choice of tempo?

5 Tap the rhythm of each hand separately. Now tap the rhythms of both hands together.

6 How will you bring this piece to life?

Going solo!

Don't forget to prepare each piece carefully before you play it.

Stage 4

Rhythmic exercises

Always count two bars before you begin each exercise (one out loud and one silently), then continue to feel the pulse strongly.

Melodic exercises

Don't forget to count two bars before you begin each melodic exercise as well.

Prepared pieces

1 What is the key of this piece? Play the scale and arpeggio.

2 Are there any scale patterns?

3 What is a tarantella?

4 What will you count? Tap the rhythm of each hand separately then both hands together.

5 Play the first note of each hand and then hear the piece through in your head.

6 How will you give a characterful performance?

Tarantella

1 What is the key of this piece? Play the scale and arpeggio.

2 Which notes are affected by the key signature?

3 Is the melody mainly in the right or left hand?

4 What will you count? Tap the rhythms of each hand separately. Then tap the rhythm of both hands together.

5 Play the first note of each hand and then hear the piece through in your head.

6 How will you give your performance character?

The chase is on!

Going solo!

Stage 5

Rhythmic exercises

Hear these rhythms in your head as well as clapping them.

Melodic exercises

Make sure you have a good idea of what each piece will sound like
before you play it.

Paul Harris' Exam Workout

Improve your sight-reading!

New editions

The ability to sight-read fluently is an important part of musical training, whether intending to play professionally, or simply for enjoyment. By becoming a good sight-reader, the player will be able to learn pieces more quickly, pianists will accompany more easily and all musicians will play duets and chamber music with confidence and assurance. Also, in grade examinations, a good performance in the sight-reading test will result in useful extra marks!

These completely new editions are designed to help incorporate sight-reading regularly into practice and lessons, and to prepare for the sight-reading test in grade examinations. They offer a progressive series of enjoyable and stimulating stages which, with careful work, should result in considerable improvement from week to week.

Step by step, the player is encouraged to build up a complete picture of each piece. Rhythmic exercises help develop and maintain a steady beat, whilst melodic exercises assist in the recognition of melodic shapes at a glance. The study of a prepared piece with associated questions for the student to answer helps consolidate acquired skills and, finally, a series of real, unprepared sight-reading tests in *Going Solo*.

Now available: two *Improve Your Sight-reading!* Piano duet books which give players a chance to practise their sight-reading skills with another player. Carefully paced to be used alongside the rest of the series.

ABRSM Editions

0-571-53300-0	Piano Pre-Grade 1
0-571-53301-9	Piano Grade 1
0-571-53302-7	Piano Grade 2
0-571-53303-5	Piano Grade 3
0-571-53304-3	Piano Grade 4
0-571-53305-1	Piano Grade 5
0-571-53306-X	Piano Grade 6
0-571-53307-8	Piano Grade 7
0-571-53308-6	Piano Grade 8
0-571-52405-2	Duets Grades 0–1
0-571-52406-0	Duets Grades 2–3

Trinity Editions

0-571-53750-2	Piano Grade Initial
0-571-53751-0	Piano Grade 1
0-571-53752-9	Piano Grade 2
0-571-53753-7	Piano Grade 3
0-571-53754-5	Piano Grade 4
0-571-53755-3	Piano Grade 5
0-571-53825-8	Electronic Keyboard Initial–Grade 1
0-571-53826-6	Electronic Keyboard Grades 2–3
0-571-53827-4	Electronic Keyboard Grades 4–5

0-571-53621-2	Violin Grade 1
0-571-53622-0	Violin Grade 2
0-571-53623-9	Violin Grade 3
0-571-53624-7	Violin Grade 4
0-571-53625-5	Violin Grade 5
0-571-53626-3	Violin Grade 6
0-571-53627-1	Violin Grades 7–8
0-571-53699-9	Viola Grades 1–5
0-571-53697-2	Cello Grades 1–3
0-571-53698-0	Cello Grades 4–5
0-571-53700-6	Double Bass Grades 1–5
0-571-51373-5	Descant Recorder Grades 1–3
0-571-51466-9	Flute Grades 1–3
0-571-51467-7	Flute Grades 4–5
0-571-51789-7	Flute Grade 6
0-571-51790-0	Flute Grades 7–8
0-571-51464-2	Clarinet Grades 1–3
0-571-51465-0	Clarinet Grades 4–5
0-571-51787-0	Clarinet Grade 6
0-571-51788-9	Clarinet Grades 7–8
0-571-51635-1	Saxophone Grades 1–3
0-571-51636-X	Saxophone Grades 4–5
0-571-51633-5	Oboe Grades 1–3
0-571-57021-6	Oboe Grades 4–5
0-571-51148-1	Bassoon Grades 1–5
0-571-51076-0	Horn Grades 1–5
0-571-50989-4	Trumpet Grades 1–5
0-571-51152-X	Trumpet Grades 5–8
0-571-56860-2	Trombone Grades 1–5

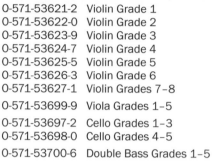

Improve your aural!

New editions

The very thought of aural, especially in examinations, strikes fear into the heart of many young pianists and instrumentalists. But aural should not be an occasional optional extra – it's something to be developing all the time, because having a good ear will help improve musicianship more than any other single musical skill.

Improve your aural! is designed to take the fear out of aural. Through fun listening activities, boxes to fill in and practice exercises, these workbooks and CDs focus on all the elements of the ABRSM aural tests. Because all aspects of musical training are of course connected, the student will also be singing, clapping, playing their instrument, writing music down, improvising and composing – as well as developing that vital ability to do well at the aural test in grade exams!

0-571-53438-4	Grade 1 (with CD)
0-571-53439-2	Grade 2 (with CD)
0-571-53544-5	Grade 3 (with CD)
0-571-53545-3	Grade 4 (with CD)
0-571-53546-1	Grade 5 (with CD)
0-571-53440-6	Grade 6 (with CD)
0-571-53441-4	Grades 7–8 (with CD)

Improve your practice!

Improve your practice! is the essential companion for pianists and instrumentalists, encapsulating Paul Harris's failsafe approach to learning. With boxes for filling in, make-your-own playing cards, a handy practice diary and an exam countdown, these books help to explore pieces and to understand their character. The books will enable the student to develop ways of getting the most out of their practice sessions – whatever their length. Most importantly, the wider musical skills such as aural, theory, sight-reading, improvisation and composition develop alongside, resulting in a more intelligent and all-round musician. Practice makes perfect!

0-571-52844-9	Piano Beginners
0-571-52261-0	Piano Grade 1
0-571-52262-9	Piano Grade 2
0-571-52263-7	Piano Grade 3
0-571-52264-5	Piano Grade 4
0-571-52265-3	Piano Grade 5
0-571-52271-8	Instrumental Grade 1
0-571-52272-6	Instrumental Grade 2
0-571-52273-4	Instrumental Grade 3
0-571-52274-2	Instrumental Grade 4
0-571-52275-0	Instrumental Grade 5

Improve your scales!

Paul Harris's *Improve your scales!* series is the only way to learn scales.

These workbooks contain not only the complete scales and arpeggios for the current ABRSM syllabus but also use finger fitness exercises, scale and arpeggio studies, key pieces and simple improvisations to help you play scales and arpeggios with real confidence.

This unique approach encourages the student to understand and play comfortably within in a key, thus helping them pick up those valuable extra marks in exams, as well as promoting a solid basis for the learning of repertoire and for sight-reading.

0-571-53411-2	Piano Grade 1
0-571-53412-0	Piano Grade 2
0-571-53413-9	Piano Grade 3
0-571-53414-7	Piano Grade 4
0-571-53415-5	Piano Grade 5
0-571-53701-4	Violin Grade 1
0-571-53702-2	Violin Grade 2
0-571-53703-0	Violin Grade 3
0-571-53704-9	Violin Grade 4
0-571-53705-7	Violin Grade 5
0-571-52024-3	Flute Grades 1–3
0-571-52025-1	Flute Grades 4–5
0-571-51475-8	Clarinet Grades 1–3
0-571-51476-6	Clarinet Grades 4–5

Improve your teaching!

Energising and inspirational, *Improve your teaching!* and *Teaching Beginners* are 'must have' handbooks for all instrumental and singing teachers. Packed full of comprehensive advice and practical strategies, they offer creative yet accessible solutions to the challenges faced in music education.

Group Music Teaching in Practice is a major resource designed to help class teachers, instrumental teachers and music services collaborate and refine their skills to enable them to deliver an holistic primary music curriculum.

These insightful volumes are distilled from years of personal experience and research. In his approachable style, Paul Harris outlines his innovative strategy of 'simultaneous learning' as well as offering advice on lesson preparation, aural and memory work, effective practice and more.

0-571-52534-2   Improve your teaching!
0-571-53175-X   Improve your teaching! Teaching beginners
0-571-53319-1   Group Music Teaching in Practice (with ECD)

The Virtuoso Teacher

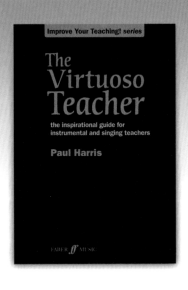

By considering *The Virtuoso Teacher* and how a teacher might attain virtuoso status, renowned educator and writer Paul Harris delves into the core issues of being a teacher and the teaching process. A fascinating look at topics such as self-awareness and the importance of emotional intelligence; getting the best out of pupils; dealing with challenging pupils; asking the right questions; creating a master-plan; taking the stress out of learning and teaching for the right reasons. This seminal book is an inspirational read for all music teachers, encouraging everyone to consider themselves in a new and uplifted light, and transform their teaching.

0-571-53676-X
The Virtuoso Teacher

The Simultaneous Learning Practice Map Pad

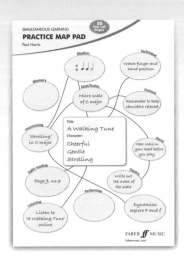

A revolutionary way to set up practice. Take a piece to be practised and write its title in the box; add words to describe the character of the piece underneath. Then set about filling in the significant features in the appropriate bubbles and begin working through these, drawing lines to make connections between them as you go along. You will achieve some really effective Simultaneous Practice!

0-571-59731-9
The Simultaneous Learning
Practice Map Pad

FABER *ff* MUSIC

Faber Music Ltd.
Burnt Mill
Elizabeth Way
Harlow
Essex
CM20 2HX

t +44 (0)1279 828982
f +44 (0)1279 828983
e sales@fabermusic.com
w www.fabermusicstore.com
  @fabermusic
  facebook.com/fabermusic

Prepared pieces

> **1** What is the key of this piece? Play the scale and arpeggio.
>
> **2** Play the tonic triad of the home key. Can you find that chord in the piece? (There are four appearances!)
>
> **3** Think about how you will finger the first four bars of the right hand.
>
> **4** Can you spot any repeated rhythmic patterns?
>
> **5** There is only one change of hand position necessary – where is it?
>
> **6** Play the first note in each hand and hear the piece in your head as best you can.

1

Tempo di valse

> **1** What is the key of this piece? Play the scale and arpeggio.
>
> **2** Where is the melody in this piece? Does it change hands?
>
> **3** Clap the left hand and think the right hand silently.
>
> **4** Can you spot any repeated patterns or patterns based on scales?
>
> **5** What does '*mesto*' mean? How will you give character to this piece?
>
> **6** Play the first note in each hand and hear the piece in your head as best you can.

2

Mesto

Going solo!

Don't forget to prepare each piece carefully before you play it.

Stage 6

Rhythmic exercises

Always count two bars before you begin each exercise –
one out loud and one silently.

Melodic exercises

And don't forget to count two bars before you begin each
melodic exercise as well.

Prepared pieces

> **1** Which hand has the melody at the start of this piece?
>
> **2** What is the name of the second note in the left hand? What is another name for this note?
>
> **3** Can you spot any repeated patterns?
>
> **4** What will you count? Tap the rhythm of each hand separately then both together.
>
> **5** Which ingredients give you clues to the character of this piece?

> **1** Does the opening phrase return anywhere?
>
> **2** What does *Andante espressivo* suggest about the character?
>
> **3** Think about an appropriate speed and establish a strong pulse in your mind.
>
> **4** What will you count? Tap the rhythm of each hand separately then both together.
>
> **5** What key is the piece in? Play the scale and arpeggio.
>
> **6** Play the first note of each hand and then hear the piece in your head as best you can.

Going solo!

Stealthily, like a cool cat

Stage 7

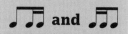

Rhythmic exercises

Clap the following two exercises many times over
until you feel really confident you know how they go.

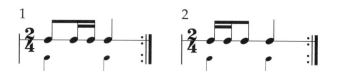

Melodic exercises

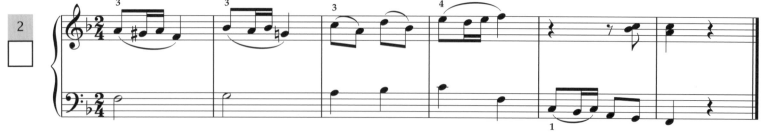

Prepared pieces

> **1** How many times does the opening rhythm (bar 1) return? Do you know exactly how it goes?
>
> **2** Which chord are bars 1 and 2 (right hand) based on?
>
> **3** What fingering will you use for the chords in the left hand, bars 1–3?
>
> **4** What key is this piece in? Play the scale and arpeggio.
>
> **5** What will you count? Tap the rhythms of each hand separately. Then tap the rhythm of both hands together.
>
> **6** What ingredients give you clues to the character of this piece?

> **1** Tapping the pulse, hear the rhythm of both hands in your head.
>
> **2** Are there any changes of hand position?
>
> **3** How many times does the rhythm of bar 1 return?
>
> **4** What is the character of this piece?
>
> **5** What is the connection between the first left-hand chord and the first two right-hand notes?
>
> **6** Play the first note of each hand and then hear the piece in your head.

Going solo!

Don't forget to prepare each piece carefully before you play it.

Stage 8

Rhythmic exercises

Always count two bars before you begin each exercise – one out loud
and one silently then continue to feel the pulse strongly.

Melodic exercises

Don't forget to count two bars before you begin
each melodic exercise as well.

Prepared pieces

1 Have a brief look at this piece and decide what the character is. What leads you to your answer?

2 Can you spot any repeated patterns – rhythmic or melodic?

3 In which key is this piece? Play the scale.

4 What will you count? Tap the rhythm of each hand separately then both together.

5 Think about the fingering. Where will you have to change hand position?

6 Play the first notes in each hand and then hear the piece in your head.

1 Think about how the character will affect the tempo you choose.

2 Can you spot any repeated patterns – rhythmic or melodic?

3 What is the key? Play the scale and arpeggio.

4 What will you count? Tap the rhythm of each hand separately then both hands together.

5 Look at the chords in the left hand bars 1-3. How will you finger them?

6 Play the first notes in each hand and then hear the piece in your head.

Going solo!

Don't forget to prepare each piece carefully before you play it.

Folk-dance

Cheerfully

Hurrying

Stage 9

Rhythmic exercises

Preparation

Here is the ideal way to prepare for sight-reading. Get into the habit of going through this checklist each time you practise your sight-reading.

1 Scan the whole piece, getting a feel for the general 'meaning'. Think about the character by noticing the various clues – tempo markings, dynamic levels, rhythm and other markings.

2 Decide what fingerings you will use at the start and notice where you will have to change hand position.

3 Try to hear the piece in your head. Don't worry about being 100% accurate – just aim to get a good overall idea of the music.

4 Feel the pulse and count in two bars before you begin.

Prepared pieces

1 Have a brief look at this piece and decide what the character is. What are the clues?

2 Can you spot any repeated patterns – rhythmic or melodic? Can you spot any scale or arpeggio patterns?

3 What will you count? Tap the rhythms of each hand separately. Then tap the rhythm of both hands together.

4 Study bars 5 and 6 for a few moments. Do you fully understand these bars?

5 Look at the chords in the right hand, bars 8-9. How are they related?

6 Play the first note and try to hear the piece in your head as best you can.

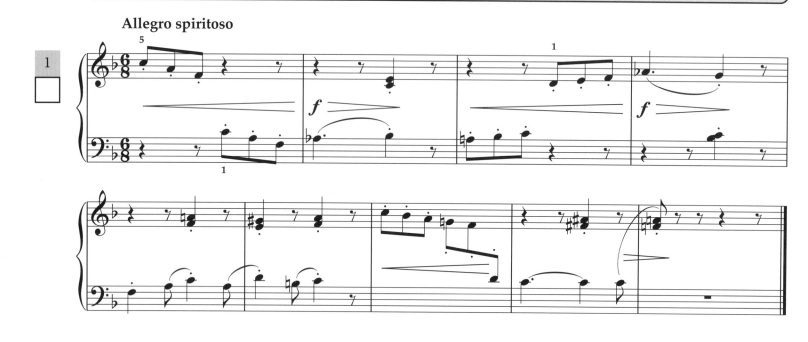

1 In what key is this piece? Play the scale and arpeggio.

2 Can you see any repeated patterns?

3 What will you count? Tap the rhythms of each hand separately. Then tap the rhythm of both hands together.

4 What do you notice about the first note in each hand?

5 What ingredients give you clues to the character of this piece?

6 Play the first note of each hand and try to hear the piece in your head as best you can.

Going solo!

Don't get your fingers in a tangle tango!

I haven't got those sight-reading blues!